LEARNING FROM
MONARCHS
A TEACHERS' HANDBOOK

by Ba Rea

BAS RELIEF, LLC
UNION, WV

Monarchs are perfect ambassadors from the natural world. They are hardy, beautiful and dramatic. The caterpillars are large and expressive, enabling them to capture the attention of the youngest learners while stretching the imaginations and inquiry skills of more sophisticated students of all ages. Their 30-day metamorphosis from egg through caterpillar and chrysalis to adult butterfly is well suited to the time frames allotted for classroom investigations. Their annual migration has attracted scientists, amateur enthusiasts, educators and the media. All these connections help to facilitate the use of monarch butterflies across the curriculum.

There are as many ways to use monarchs in the classroom as there are teachers interested in giving it a try. They offer a compelling introduction to insect life cycles, the intricacies of ecosystems and food webs, and the balance of nature. They can be the focus of a profound inquiry science project, complete with math and graphing skills, which can connect students with an international community of citizen scientists. They can also be an exciting journaling theme, a catalyst for understanding geography and human culture, a dynamic study in ethics, and a wonderful subject for art and design. This text is intended as a starting point for teachers interested in using monarchs in their classrooms. It introduces concepts and information that will be useful as you design your own monarch lessons.

CONTENTS

AUTHOR'S NOTE

Each "monarch" person I meet has a different story. Each story confirms my suspicion that these delightful insects are true ambassadors from the natural world to our species. I am telling you my monarch story, hoping you either have one of your own or soon will.

In the summer of 1970, when I first encountered monarch caterpillars, I was not interested in their roles in science or curriculum. They became a connection to the mysteries of nature that gave meaning to my life. I was actually on a very informal botany quest, trying to understand how a milkweed umbel full of pink, fleshy florets was going to turn into the fuzz and seed filled milkweed pods with which I was familiar. The smooth-skinned, striped caterpillars with the bouncy, black, antenna-like protrusions front and back were a surprise. As I searched the milkweed patch I found tiny replicas of the bigger caterpillars that originally attracted my attention. I brought them home on the milkweed. I didn't try to contain them. They were part of the bouquet I was watching and drawing. Finding a fully formed, gold speckled, jade-green monarch chrysalis hanging from the edge of a dresser was a complete surprise. I started watching the caterpillars more closely. I didn't know to watch for a caterpillar in "J." I don't think that I had the good fortune of catching a caterpillar in transition to chrysalis that first summer, but when the chrysalides I located started turning orange and black, I made a point of sticking around to watch for the emergence of the butterfly. What magic!

Each summer after that I hunted for a milkweed patch and monarchs to watch. For 16 years I was oblivious of all of the other people watching monarchs. When the success of Dr. Fred Urquhart's continent wide search for the over-wintering destination of the monarch butterfly migration burst onto the front cover of National Geographic in 1976, I was only mildly interested. For me the beauty and the magic of the metamorphosis of the caterpillars into butterflies was enough. That didn't change until my kids were old enough to start sharing in my annual obsession.

Since then I have become more and more active with the human monarch community. I've tagged monarchs. I've had the pleasure of attending two monarch butterfly conferences and meeting monarch butterfly enthusiasts and scientists from all over the world. I've worked with many teachers and attended monarch celebrations from Pittsburgh, Pennsylvania to Eagle Pass, Texas. I travelled to the butterfly reserves. At La Chincua in February of 2002, I walked across the forest floor strewn with dead and moribund monarchs. I was amazed by the devastation the January storms had wrought, but encouraged by the monarchs still clustering high in the oyamel firs. I was delighted by their comeback the very next season.

Every year I learn more. Through each project, book and trip, monarchs open up my world. May they do the same for you.

Ba Rea

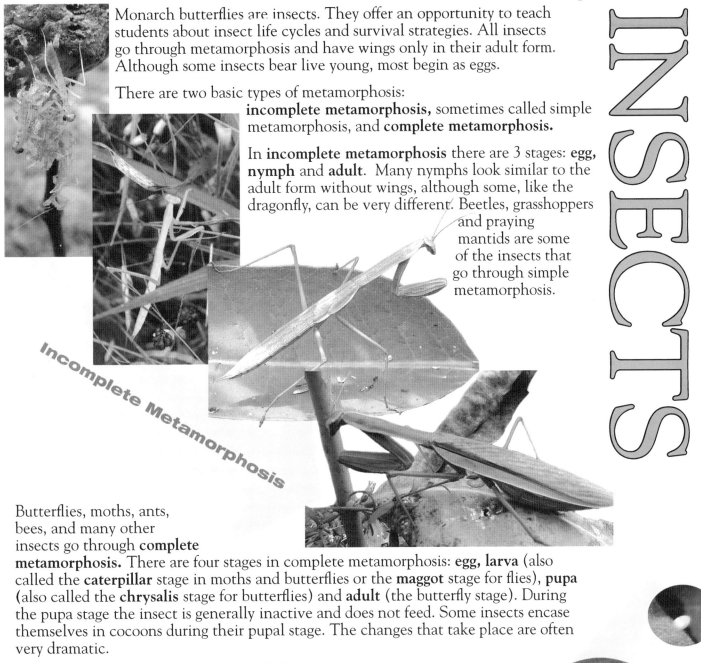

Monarch butterflies are insects. They offer an opportunity to teach students about insect life cycles and survival strategies. All insects go through metamorphosis and have wings only in their adult form. Although some insects bear live young, most begin as eggs.

There are two basic types of metamorphosis: **incomplete metamorphosis,** sometimes called simple metamorphosis, and **complete metamorphosis.**

In **incomplete metamorphosis** there are 3 stages: **egg, nymph** and **adult.** Many nymphs look similar to the adult form without wings, although some, like the dragonfly, can be very different. Beetles, grasshoppers and praying mantids are some of the insects that go through simple metamorphosis.

INSECTS

Incomplete Metamorphosis

Butterflies, moths, ants, bees, and many other insects go through **complete metamorphosis.** There are four stages in complete metamorphosis: **egg, larva** (also called the **caterpillar** stage in moths and butterflies or the **maggot** stage for flies), **pupa** (also called the **chrysalis** stage for butterflies) and **adult** (the butterfly stage). During the pupa stage the insect is generally inactive and does not feed. Some insects encase themselves in cocoons during their pupal stage. The changes that take place are often very dramatic.

Complete Metamorphosis

Monarch caterpillar with recently shed cuticle

All insects have **exoskeletons.** This tough layer, also called a **cuticle,** protects them and supports their bodies, much as skeletons do for us. Insect exoskeletons do not grow. Nymphs and larvae are the growing stages of insects. As they grow, they molt their exoskeletons several times. The stages between molts are referred to as **instars.** A first instar caterpillar is one that has hatched from its egg but not yet molted. A second instar caterpillar has molted once. Different insects go through different numbers of instars. Monarch caterpillars go through 5 instars before forming a chrysalis. As well as getting larger, caterpillars at each successive instar have different markings. Sometimes the differences are subtle and sometimes they are dramatic.

All insects, at all stages, have three body parts: the **head, thorax** and **abdomen.**

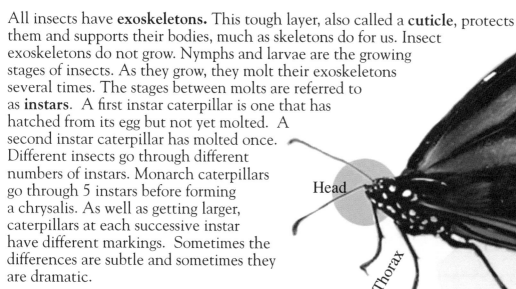

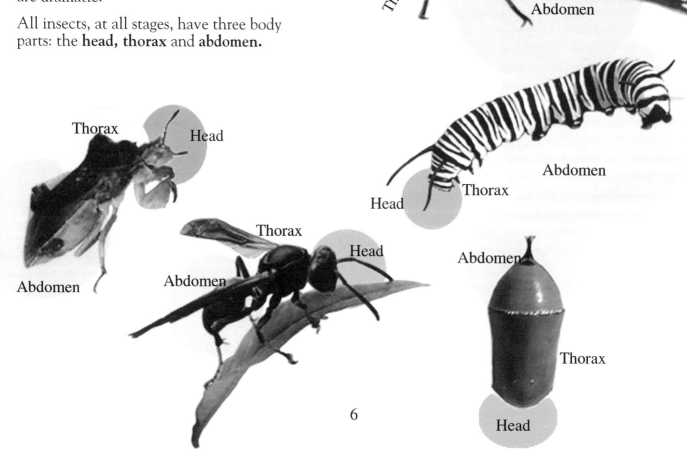

Compound eye

Ocelli

Eyes, mouthparts and antennae are located on an insect's head. Insects have two kinds of eyes, **compound** and simple eyes called **ocelli.** Most adult insects have a compound eye on either side of their heads and three ocelli in the center of their heads between the compound eyes. Larvae of insects that go through complete metamorphosis do not have compound eyes.

Proboscis

Insect **antennae** are usually located on the front of the head below the ocelli. Antennae are distinctive and are often used to identify insect groups.

Monarch butterfly

There are many variations in insect mouthparts, but they are usually adapted for either chewing or sucking. Chewing mouths, like those of the monarch caterpillar, have **mandibles** that move from side to side. Sucking mouthparts are highly modified mandibles. Butterflies and moths have a long, straw-like **proboscis** which is held coiled beneath their heads when not in use. Careful observation of an adult monarch butterfly's proboscis will reveal that it is made up of two mouthparts knitted together. Other insects have sucking mouthparts that enclose a stylet for piercing. This type of mouth is called a **rostrum.** Bees have chewing mandibles with a beak-like tongue to suck liquid.

Milkweed Bug

Rostrum

Praying Mantis

Mandibles

Pennsylvania
Leatherwing

All insects have six legs attached to the thorax. Most adult insects also have two pairs of wings attached to the thorax. Flies are called **dipterans** which means two wings. Although they have just two wings, close examination will reveal tiny paddle-like structures called **halteres**, where the second set of wings would have been. Others, like ants and aphids, only have wings under special circumstances such as dispersal or mating.

The thickheaded fly is a dipteran with one pair of wings and two halteres

Monarch butterfly
brush feet

Monarch butterflies appear to have only four legs. They are members of the family Nymphalidae—the brush foot butterflies. The first pair of legs on brush foot butterflies are very small. They are kept tucked up close to the thorax. They are used for tasting. If you are able to closely observe a female monarch looking for a place to lay eggs you might see her drumming on the milkweed with her tiny front legs. She is tasting it, perhaps to decide whether it is the plant on which she wants to lay her eggs.

7

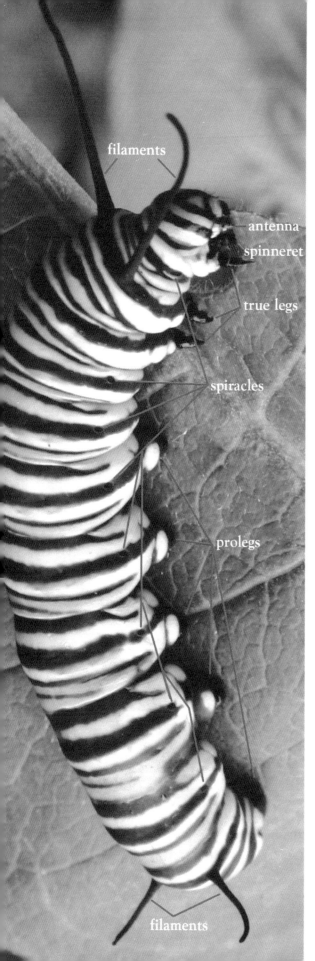

filaments

antenna

spinneret

true legs

spiracles

prolegs

filaments

Caterpillars, and some other insect larvae, appear to have too many legs. If you observe closely you will notice 3 pairs of hard true legs at the front of the body. All of the true legs are attached to the thorax of the caterpillar. Five pairs of prolegs are part of the abdomen of the larvae. These legs are soft and puffy and end in little hooks called crochets. They help the larval stage of the insect get around. Insect abdomens are segmented and, in the adult form, usually have no appendages except at the end, which may have clasper-like or feeler-like cerci or ovipositors.

Insects breathe through a network of tubes that bring oxygen directly to their tissues. The external openings to the respiratory tubes are called **spiracles**. There are usually two on the thorax and many on the abdomen. Spiracles can be easily located on the caterpillar, chrysalis and adult monarch butterfly. Insect circulatory systems are open with no veins or arteries. A tube in the abdomen pumps blood, called hemolymph, throughout their bodies.

Insects can detect touch, chemicals, sound, light and vibration. Many of their sensory organs are located in their body walls. Drum-like structures and special hairs are sensitive to sound waves pitched much higher than the sounds we hear. Taste and smell receptors are located on the mouthparts, antennae and feet.

Egg

Every monarch begins its life as an egg laid one at a time on some part of a milkweed plant. A monarch egg is creamy white with ridges and tapers to a point at the top. When milkweed is scarce, as in the early spring or in a captive setting, monarchs may load a single plant with eggs, but under most circumstances they will lay just one egg per plant. It is easy to mistake hardened bubbles of latex, the milky white sap of milkweed plants, for monarch eggs. Gently run your finger over the top of the "egg." If it is really an egg you will feel the point at the top. If it is latex it will be smooth and will often fall off extremely easily. Most monarch eggs are securely fastened to the leaf, pod, stem or bud. Most eggs are laid on the underside of tender young leaves. However, it is not unusual to find them anywhere on the milkweed plant. Sometimes a female butterfly will develop a unique "style" of egg laying. When that happens you will likely find many of her eggs laid in the same unusual way.

If the temperature is in the upper 60s or 70s(F), the eggs will usually hatch in three to five days. Just before they hatch you may notice that the top of the egg has turned dark. If you use a magnifying glass and watch the black spot, it may move or disappear. It is the head capsule of the caterpillar inside and the caterpillar can move around inside the egg!

CATERPILLAR

Caterpillars are the larval stage of butterflies and moths. The head, thorax and abdomen can be easily distinguished. On a larger caterpillar it is possible to see the **spiracles** with which it breathes, its **antennae,** and the **mandibles** with which it chews its food. The caterpillar's six true legs are attached to the thoracic segments. Five pairs of fleshy **prolegs**, that end in tiny hooks called **crochets**, can be found on the abdomen. On 2nd through 5th instar monarch caterpillars a pair of fleshy **filaments** can be found on the thorax and another pair on the abdomen.

Newly hatched 1st instar monarch caterpillars usually eat the shell of the egg they emerge from first. They then eat the hairs on the leaf and then the milkweed leaf itself in an arched pattern around the spot on which they are standing. The milkweed sap is sticky and can be dangerous for a newly hatched caterpillar. By eating in an arch the caterpillar severs the tiny veins in the leaf around it and sets up a sap-free zone to munch on without fear of more bubbles of latex.

If a 1st instar caterpillar falls off of its milkweed plant, it needs to be able to get back to it. Just below the caterpillar's head is a spinneret, much like the spinnerets that spiders use to spin their webs. Immediately upon hatching the caterpillar begins to adhere the sticky silk thread from its spinneret to the milkweed leaf as it eats and travels. If the leaf is jostled and the caterpillar falls, it can climb the silk thread back to the leaf.

Late first instar caterpillar. The head capsule is all black. Notice the barely visible stubby filaments in front and the circular eating pattern on the milkweed.

The caterpillar eats, grows and produces copious amounts of **frass** (caterpillar solid waste) until it is too big for its **cuticle**. The cuticle is the equivalent of the adult exoskeleton and it does not grow. The caterpillar must shed it to keep growing. A caterpillar about to shed stays in a fairly small area moving back and forth and not eating. It is creating a mat of silk threads on the surface (usually a leaf) below it. Inside the caterpillar, its new cuticle is forming. Enzymes are being secreted which break down the old cuticle. On a larger, 3rd or 4th instar caterpillar you can, with a magnifying glass, see the new cuticle wrinkled up and waiting below the transparent old cuticle. When everything is ready, the caterpillar will hook the **crochets** on its **prolegs** into the silk mat below it. Its **head capsule** will pop off and the caterpillar, in its new cuticle will crawl out of the old "skin." Except in the case of the very tiny all black 1st instar head capsule, it is relatively easy to search through the **frass** (caterpillar solid waste) in the bottom of its container to find the discarded head capsule of a newly molted monarch caterpillar. The caterpillar will shed its cuticle four times. The length of time the caterpillar will spend in each instar will be affected by the quantity and quality of food available, moisture and temperature. If temperatures are in the upper 60° to mid 70° F range a monarch caterpillar will be ready to pupate fourteen to eighteen days after the egg is laid.

Early instar caterpillars seem to eat mostly during daylight hours, but by the time the caterpillar is in the fifth instar it will likely eat all day and night. As it eats the caterpillar will produce copious amounts of **frass** .

Later instar caterpillars develop some different defenses than early instar caterpillars as well. When disturbed by a loud noise or being touched, a late instar monarch caterpillar will jerk its head and thorax back repeatedly to "scare" away an intruder. If it is picked up or otherwise really disturbed, it will curl into a ball.

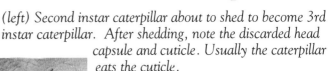

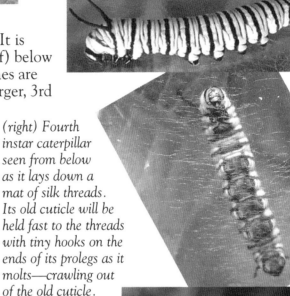

(left) Second instar caterpillar about to shed to become 3rd instar caterpillar. After shedding, note the discarded head capsule and cuticle. Usually the caterpillar eats the cuticle.

(below) Fourth instar caterpillar ready to shed. The old head capsule is detached and sticking to the caterpillar's new head capsule.

(right) Fourth instar caterpillar seen from below as it lays down a mat of silk threads. Its old cuticle will be held fast to the threads with tiny hooks on the ends of its prolegs as it molts—crawling out of the old cuticle.

(right) Fifth instar caterpillar

11

HANGING IN "J"

When a monarch caterpillar is ready to pupate it will lay down a silk mat like it did each time it shed. This time the mat is on a surface from which the caterpillar will be able to hang. It will spend a good deal of time in the middle of the mat spinning a silk button.

Caterpillar creating silk button

When it is ready, the caterpillar will walk past the silk button and grasp it with its last prolegs. Letting go with all other legs, the caterpillar hangs upside down from the silk button. Its head and true legs contract and bend upward. The caterpillar is said to be hanging in "J." It will hang this way for 18 hours or more. Inside changes that have been going on for days are continuing. The caterpillar's filaments go limp as the body is retracted out of them. If you shine a light through the skin near where the last prolegs are holding onto the silk button you can see that, inside, the body has been pulled away from the prolegs. The black, stick-like **cremaster** of the chrysalis is visible. As with previous moltings, enzymes are secreted that break down the cuticle. Eventually the caterpillar cuticle splits behind its head. The bright green form of the monarch chrysalis begins to wriggle, forcing the old caterpillar cuticle to bunch up. Two tiny, rough protrusions called **holdfast tubercles** hold onto the old cuticle as it collects near the silk button. The monarch pulls its cremaster out of the wad of old cuticle and drives it into the silk button. It writhes violently, driving the hooks at the end of the cremaster into the silk button. The old cuticle drops away. The new chrysalis form will continue to writhe and contract for half an hour or more.

Caerpillar gasping the silk button and letting go

Cremaster

holdfast tubercle

CHRYSALIS

A crease in the segment below the six dots under the cremaster indicates a chrysalis is a female.

Male   Female

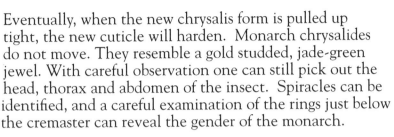

Eventually, when the new chrysalis form is pulled up tight, the new cuticle will harden. Monarch chrysalides do not move. They resemble a gold studded, jade-green jewel. With careful observation one can still pick out the head, thorax and abdomen of the insect. Spiracles can be identified, and a careful examination of the rings just below the cremaster can reveal the gender of the monarch.

The chrysalis will hang this way for about 10 days. Near the end of the chrysalis stage the pigment and form of the new butterfly will become visible through the clear cuticle. Once again enzymes will be secreted to break down the cuticle and the new butterfly will begin to **eclose**—that is to emerge from the chrysalis cuticle.

BUTTERFLY

1

An elongated triangular piece of the chrysalis cuticle opens up first, allowing the new butterfly to stretch its legs and free its newly formed, **proboscis** and antennae from the cuticle. The proboscis is a mouth designed for sucking nectar. It separates from the cuticle in two pieces that the butterfly knits together in the first few minutes after eclosing. The butterfly form will pull out of the cuticle and swing down to hang from the new **tarsi**—butterfly feet. Its wings will be shriveled and bright and its abdomen bloated. Strong contractions will begin to ripple across the abdomen, forcing **hemolymph** (butterfly blood) into the wings and expanding them. The butterfly must continue to hang with its wings pulled down by gravity while they expand. Fully expanded wings will still be soft and damp. A small amount of red fluid will leak out of the butterfly's digestive system. This is the last of the caterpillar frass. The new butterfly used the frass to help build pressure to pump hemolymph into its wings and is now releasing it. It will take another hour or two before the wings harden and the butterfly begins to open and close them. In time the new butterfly will let go of its perch and fly away. Its new body is still changing and developing. It is not unusual for the butterfly not to eat for a day or two. It will not mate for several days. If it is a member of the migrating generation of monarchs for the season it will not mate for several months. It will begin its migration to the over-wintering sites.

2

3

4

MIGRATION

Insects are cold blooded. They cannot maintain their body temperature when the temperatures drop. All insects must have a strategy for surviving harsh winter temperatures. Some over-winter underground, some make cocoons and pupate, some over-winter as eggs or egg cases. Monarch butterflies migrate. Those that eclose from April until August live an average of four weeks. They nectar, mate, and the females lay eggs. There is speculation that they may also be continuously heading northward.

At some point in August, most eclosing monarch butterflies will be in **reproductive diapause.** Diapausal butterflies are sexually immature and have a greater amount of lipid (fat) cells. There is also anecdotal observation that they tend to orient higher in the air column. The timing of the change over to diapause is correlated to the angle of the sun at noon at each particular latitude. For instance, in western Pennsylvania monarchs eclosing after August 15th tend to be in diapause. Butterflies in Toronto would tend to be diapausal a bit earlier, those in Union, West Virginia a little later.

Map of the fall migration

Migrating monarchs clustering at an evening roost in Eagle Pass, Texas

Children watching butterflies "puddling" (drinking water and getting minerals) in the El Rosario Butterfly Reserve in Michoacan, Mexico.

Close up of large clusters of butterflies at El Rosario, Michoacan, Mexico (far right) and visitors walking beneath them

14

Scientists studying the monarchs (left) and clusters of monarchs at Pismo Beach in California (right).

Monarch butterflies east of the continental divide in North America migrate to an area in the oyamel fir forests above nine thousand feet in Michoacan, Mexico. As they pour out of the north they can be found clustering on hedgerows and in trees as they make their way south. Like hawks, they fly high and catch thermals to help them along their way. On the west coast, diapausal monarch butterflies arrive to cluster in pines and eucalyptus trees in several sites near the coast of California. There are still many unanswered questions about the logistics of the migration. We know that the butterflies are seeking out an area with relatively low temperatures and not too much or too little humidity, to wait out the winter. On sunny days during the winter, the butterflies will come out of the trees to nectar and to collect minerals by drinking water from puddles and moist soil.

Successful butterflies will begin to mate and migrate north again in late February and early March. Monarch butterflies in Hawaii and on other islands that do not experience harsh winters do not seem to produce a diapausal phase. Diapausal butterflies that are kept at high temperatures (80°F and above), will break diapause and become reproductive. Regardless of how they break diapause, as soon as they become reproductive the butterflies will live an average of 4 more weeks.

Map of the spring migration

THE MONARCH-MILKWEED COMMUNITY

The milkweed patch where monarchs begin their lives is a robust community. It provides an excellent opportunity to introduce students to the concepts of habitat, community and food webs. Students can learn to use field guides as well. Each milkweed patch will share some features with other milkweed patches and have other aspects that are unique. Climate and local species of milkweed vary widely across the country. The photographs and species covered here are for the most part from communities in the northeastern United States. There are some unique qualities from southern and western communities that are not covered in this edition.

HABITATS AND COMMUNITIES

Every living thing needs food, water, air, and space in a particular configuration often including shelter. The physical place where an organism gets all of those things is called its **habitat.** The milkweed patch is the monarch caterpillar's habitat. Habitats overlap. The milkweed patch is habitat for many other organisms as well. All of the organisms that exist in an area are referred to as a **community**. Healthy communities are in a dynamic balance.

FOOD WEBS

One of the clearest models of a community is a **food web**. In this model the community is represented by connecting each organism to those from which it obtains its energy and to those which obtain their energy from it. Understanding an organism's role in the food web will help you understand the story playing out in the milkweed patch.

Energy flows through communities. Each time it moves from one organism to the next a little energy is lost. With only a few exceptions (like organisms living near thermal vents on the mid ocean ridges) energy initially enters every community as sunlight. The energy from sunlight is captured by green plants through a process called **photosynthesis.** Since it is the sugars that they make from sunlight that fuel the community, plants are called **producers**. A community needs a lot of producers. Animals that eat plants

This is a very simplified food web. The arrows are pointing in the direction of the flow of the energy (ie an arrow point from the food source TO the organism that consumes it). In a more complete model, there would be more individuals representing each kind of organism in the community.

16

are called **herbivores**. **Nectivores** are a specialized type of herbivore that drinks nectar from plants. The **biomass** of herbivores is less than the biomass of the producers in a community. **Predators** eat herbivores, nectivores and other animals. Predators that eat mostly insects are called **insectivores.** A community can support more herbivores than predators. Organisms that live in or on other living organisms are called **parasites.** **Scavengers** are organisms that eat dead organisms, waste and discarded body parts. In the real world some organisms have multiple roles. For instance, ants can act as predators, nectivores and scavengers.

A change in any part of a food web, as in nature, affects all other parts of the web. The following is a walk through the milkweed patch to get your ideas flowing.

PRODUCERS

MILKWEED

Milkweed is the host plant for a number of organisms. Its fragrant blossoms attract many nectivores and all that activity attracts many predators. Plants frequently found among the milkweeds, like ironweed, goldenrod, wild asters and joe pye weed attract their own set of herbivores and nectivores as well making the community even richer. A trip to a local milkweed patch can be a starting point for learning about the diversity of local insects and spiders and their many interesting and unique life styles.

Plants of the milkweed family are the host plants for monarch butterflies. In the caterpillar stage they eat milkweed and sequester the cardiac glycosides found in its sap. The poisons are retained in the exoskeleton of the adult, making them unpalatable to most birds and mammals. The toxicity of milkweed plants is quite variable by species. The varieties of the north eastern U.S.— Common Milkweed (*Asclepias syriaca*), Swamp Milkweed (*Asclepias incarnata*) and

Swamp Milkweed, *Asclepias incarnata* to the left; Common Milkweed, *Asclepias syriaca* to the right and above.

17

MILKWEED (continued)

Butterfly Weed (*Asclepias tuberosa*)— are less toxic than some of their southern cousins like Tropical Milkweed (*Asclepias curassavica*). Tropical Milkweed is finding its way into our gardens through nurseries. In the north it is sold as an annual and cannot survive winter. However, in southern states it is becoming established. There are 110 species of milkweed in the continental United States. Worldwide there are 2-3000 species.

Umbels of tropical milkweed, *Asclepias curassavica*

Umbel of common milkweed *Asclepias syriaca*

Milkweed flowers can be white, green, red, orange, pink or purple. They bloom in an umbel, a cluster of flowers with flower stalks all arising from a central point. The umbels can be tight balls of flowers or a loose spray of blooms.

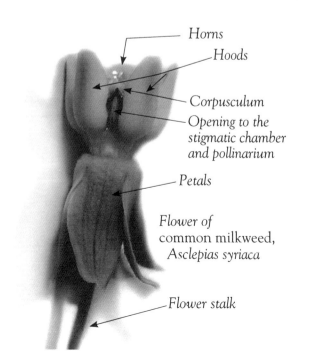

Umbels of butterfly weed, *Asclepias tuberosa*

What is unique about the flowers is their system for delivering pollen to fertilize their seeds. Each milkweed flower in an umbel has five modified anthers that form hoods and horns. The hoods contain nectar to attract insects and are arranged around a central flower column. Five petals fall back against the flower stalk. There are slits in the flower column created by flaps of the modified anthers. Inside each slit are both the opening to the stigmatic chamber where pollen must be delivered to fertilize the seeds and a

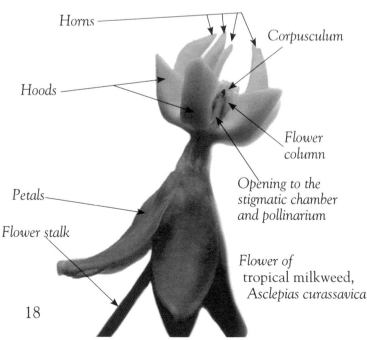

Horns

Hoods

Corpusculum

Opening to the stigmatic chamber and pollinarium

Petals

Flower of common milkweed, *Asclepias syriaca*

Flower stalk

Horns

Corpusculum

Hoods

Flower column

Opening to the stigmatic chamber and pollinarium

Petals

Flower stalk

Flower of tropical milkweed, *Asclepias curassavica*

18

Pollinarium

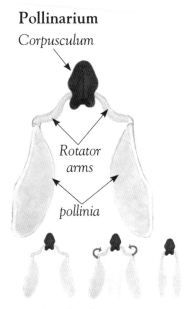

Corpusculum

Rotator arms

pollinia

As they dry the rotator arms turn the pollinia 90°

uniquely evolved structure, called a pollinarium, which has evolved to carry the flower's pollen.

The pollinarium is wishbone shaped. At the top is a clip called a corpusculum. It is a dark spot that can easily be seen in the slit on the flower column. Hanging from the corpusculum are two sacks each full of enough pollen to fertilize all of the seeds in an entire milkweed pod. The sacks are called pollinia. They are attached to the corpusculum by threads called rotator arms. When an insect lands on the flower to drink nectar, its leg or antennae or even bristles on its body slip into the slit on the flower column. The corpusculum clips on to the body parts as the insects pulls them free. When milkweed is in bloom, often you will see many pollinia attached to the legs of the nectaring insects. Occasionally you will also find an insect that was too small or weak to pull the pollinia out of the flower column dangling from a milkweed flower, its leg held fast by the corpusculum. It will die either from starvation and exhaustion or by becoming prey for one of the many predators lurking about in the milkweed patch.

Dead bee trapped on a milkweed flower

If an insect is a successful pollinator, the pollinia attached to its leg will slip back into the slit on another flower column as it continues to nectar. Most milkweed plants need pollen from another plant to fertilize their seeds. The pollinia play a fascinating role in this process, assuring that their pollen gets to another plant. When the pollinarium is first pulled out of the flower column, the rotator arms hold the pollinia out away from each other. In that position it would be hard for the pollinia to slip into a flower column. As they dry, the rotator arms turn the pollinia 90° until they are lined up next to each other ready to slip back into a flower column. This takes a while so the insect has time to move on to a flower on another milkweed plant!

DOGBANE

Dogbane is related to milkweed. It often grows in the same places common milkweed grows. With its milky sap and rounded leaves, it is easily mistaken for common milkweed. If you happen to see it flowering you will notice that it's flowers are not milkweed flowers. Two other ways to tell it apart are:

- Its stems are very smooth and often red or burgundy

- It branches.

Common milkweed will branch when the terminal bud—the bud at the very end of the stem— has been removed or if it is diseased, but will not normally branch otherwise. Monarchs cannot eat dogbane.

Dogbane

HERBIVORES
COMPETING CONSUMERS

Monarch caterpillars are herbivores. They eat the leaves, flowers and pods of milkweed. There are several other insects that eat milkweed. Organisms that depend on the same food source are called **competing consumers**.

Tussock moth caterpillars (*Euchaetias egle*) with their wild brown, black and white tufts are a common sight in the milkweed patch.

The eggs are laid in fuzz covered masses. Their strategy to stay together as early instar caterpillars makes them a particularly potent competitor for monarchs. As they move over the milkweed plant skeletonizing it, the mass of caterpillars will likely eat any solitary monarch egg in their path. In early instars they can be found as large masses of pale caterpillars. As they grow they develop tufts and become more solitary.

In early to mid-June, **milkweed longhorn beetles** (*Tetraopes sp.*) emerging from underground pupation start appearing on milkweed plants. They characteristically eat the tips of leaves and milkweed flower buds. By late June they begin mating. The females lay their eggs at the base of milkweed stems. The beetle larvae burrow into the ground and feed on the roots of milkweed plants until they pupate in the spring.

Large milkweed bug
(*Oncopeltus fasciatus*)

Milkweed bugs over-winter in detritus and can be found on milkweed plants by mid-June to early July. Clusters of milkweed bug nymphs, tended by adults can often be found on milkweed pods throughout the fall.

The large milkweed bug (*Oncopeltus fasciatus*) is an herbivore that eats seeds when they are available. To identify large milkweed bugs look for the solid black band across its back.

Small milkweed bug
(*Lygaeus kalmii*)

The small milkweed bug (*Lygaeus kalmii*) has diversified. Though they too prefer eating milkweed seeds, they have been observed eating other plant matter, dead insects and even preying on other insects. To identify a small milkweed bug look for the red "X" on its back.

21

Swamp milkweed leaf beetles (*Labidomera clivicollis*) eat milkweed but are usually not as plentiful as longhorn milkweed beetles or milkweed bugs. Yellow to red oblong eggs are laid in clusters on milkweed leaves, often swamp milkweed. The larvae can be beige to pink to bright red. They grow quickly and drop to the ground to pupate. The adults look a little like large ladybugs with larger, irregular black spots that form an X across their backs. The larvae suffer heavy predation and are most often found on swamp milkweed. A study of their predators showed that many were insects that walk from one site to another. The study concluded that swamp milkweed, which sometimes grows standing in water, might afford them a little bit of protection.

Yellow Oleander aphids (*Aphis nerii*) are common on milkweed plants where they suck sap. This species of aphids does not produce a mating generation with males at the end of the season like most aphids. They are always all female.

The nymphs and adults of some **plant hoppers** of the family Flatidae can be found feeding on milkweed. They suck juices from the plants and can transmit diseases like phytoplasm from one plant to another.

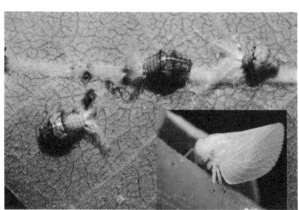

A common milkweed plant suffering from phytoplasmosis likely spread by planthoppers. Note the branching and the wrinkling and yellowing of the leaves.

Bumblebee on common milkweed

NECTIVORES

Nectivores are specialized herbivores that drink nectar. During blooming season milkweed attracts many nectivores including the monarch butterfly. Many kinds of butterflies and moths, as well as honeybees, carpenter bees, bumblebees and many flies hover around the sweet blossoms. Some, like the Pennsylvania leatherwing beetle, sip the nectar and eat the pollen clinging to their legs, as well. All of this activity attracts many predators.

Honeybee on common milkweed

Flies on common milkweed

Leatherwing beetle eating pollinia clinging to his legs

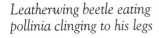

Fritillaries on purple milkweed (Asclepias purpurascens)

INCIDENTAL HERBIVORES

Many of the insects found in the milkweed patch are just passing through. They stop to rest on the milkweed plants and may fall prey to predators there. They are often attracted to other nearby vegetation.

This grasshopper nymph is just hanging out. It will go elsewhere for food.

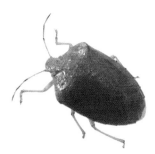

Green stinkbugs are herbivores but some other stinkbugs are predators.

Leaf-footed bugs look formidable but they are harmless herbivores.

PREDATORS

Ladybug beetles (family Coccinellidae) of many different kinds prowl milkweed patches. In both the adult and larval phases of their lives they are formidable predators. Many species of ladybugs prey on one or two specific organisms, like aphids or white flies.

Ladybug larva

24

A well camouflaged ambush bug (family Phymatidae) hides in milkweed flowers capturing passing nectivores. Check out the leaves below for discarded insect body parts and the scavengers who are eating or collecting them.

A petite long-legged fly (family Dolichopodidae) scurries over leaves looking for small soft bodied insects, like young caterpillars, to eat.

A praying mantis rests on a common milkweed leaf waiting for prey to pass by. It'll capture wasps, bees, grasshoppers and butterflies.

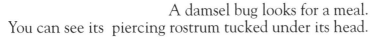

A damsel bug looks for a meal. You can see its piercing rostrum tucked under its head.

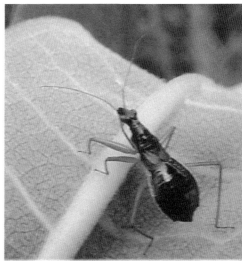

25

A wheel bug, from the assassin bug family, is an aggressive predator. It stabs its victims, paralyzing them and dissolving their tissues with saliva. Then it sucks the fluid out of the wound. Note the rostrum (or beak) tucked under its head.

There are many spiders in the milkweed patch. They will catch caterpillars and butterflies as well as many other insects.

A jumping spider has captured a monarch caterpillar. They attack and eat insects much larger than themselves.

Garden spiders and their familiar webs with a central hub and radiating "spokes" are common in the milkweed patch, especially in the fall.

A nursery web spider clings to a milkweed stem. Her egg case is carefully wrapped in a milkweed leaf above her.

Camouflaged in the flowers, crab spiders are laying in wait for passing nectivores to eat. Check out the leaves below a crab spider to see discarded insect body parts and the scavengers who are eating or collecting them.

PARASITES

Tachinid flies search for caterpillars on which they lay their eggs. The maggots hatch, burrow into the unsuspecting caterpillar and proceed to devour it from the inside out.

The maggots usually leave behind a telltale thread on the dead chrysalis.

maggot

Pupae

Thickheaded flies (family Conopidae) nectar on the milkweed flowers while watching for bees and wasps on which they lay their eggs.

SCAVENGERS

Sow bugs are scavengers, scurrying about in the soil beneath the milkweed plants. On damp mornings they will be on the plant looking for dead plant and animal matter.

AND OPPORTUNISTS

Many insects have more than one role in the milkweed patch.

This syrphid fly is a nectivore, but its larva is a fierce predator (especially if you happen to be an aphid!).

Harvesters, also called daddy long legs, drink nectar, scavenge and capture slow moving prey.

Ants have a multitude of roles in the milkweed patch. They are nectivores, scavengers and predators. They are even farmers. Ants will often tend a "herd" of aphids, protecting them from predators and "milking" them for the sweet honeydew that they produce.

Ants scavenging discarded body parts dropped by an ambush bug

Soldier beetles like this Pennsylvania leatherwing eat nectar and pollen from the milkweed flowers but they also prey on aphids and any soft bodied insects.

Ants farming aphids

This earwig is a scavenger, nectivore and sometimes a predator too.

This paper wasp drinks nectar and eats pollen, but she also is hunting for caterpillars which she will cut up and stuff in her nest to feed her young.

The milkweed patch is a very busy place!

28

ACQUIRING STOCK

The first issue for using monarchs in the classroom is the obvious one. Where will you get your stock? Two possibilities are collecting in the field and buying stock from breeders. You can also purchase and breed your own butterflies, but outlining the logistics for that is beyond the scope of this introduction. Once you have decided how you will get your stock you must determine when you will get it. Keep in mind the timing you will need in your classroom for the caterpillar lesson you are planning. It's a good idea to work some flexibility into your plans as living creatures have a way of developing in their own time, not on your schedule!

At temperatures between 70 and 80 degrees Fahrenheit:

- Eggs will hatch in 4 days or less.
- Caterpillars will shed four times and be ready to pupate in 14 or less days.
- Butterflies will emerge from chrysalides after 8 to 14 days

Collecting in the Field

Collecting in the field can be quite satisfying. If students are able to find the eggs and caterpillars themselves they can develop a much clearer understanding of the monarch's natural community. However, finding wild monarchs is not always possible. It can be time consuming and, in years in which the monarch population is low or spotty, it can be frustrating. Some parts of the country have a more reliable monarch population than others. And depending on your latitude monarchs may already be becoming scarce as the school year begins or not yet arrived as it ends.

If your conditions are good and you are interested in trying to collect monarchs for use in your classroom, you should start identifying and monitoring likely milkweed patches in your area early in the season. Caterpillars will likely become more plentiful toward the end of the breeding season due to a growing population of butterflies, but will start to taper off as newly eclosed butterflies begin emerging in reproductive diapause. A patch may not produce the same quantities of caterpillars or even the same quantity and quality of milkweed every year. The number of available caterpillars will be dependent on the number of monarchs laying eggs in the area and in the patches you search. The condition of the milkweed and the how much predation there is in that area that year will affect the number of caterpillars or eggs you will find as well.

Think about how you will transport your caterpillars before you go hunting. You'll need to keep the caterpillars contained and the milkweed moist so it doesn't wilt. Wide mouthed plastic jars and

disposable food containers work well. Shoebox sized plastic boxes in a backpack work. There are even collapsible bug tents that you can easily carry into the field. Small containers for leaves with eggs are a good idea. Carry a little water with you for the milkweed. Lay damp paper towels in the bottom of the container or carry them in a plastic bag to use to keep milkweed leaves fresh until you get them back to your main containers.

Containers used by restaurants for leftovers and take-out salads are good for hatching eggs.

What to Look For and Where to Look

5th instar caterpillar leaving typical arched chew holes on the edges of milkweed leaves

When looking for stock in the wild, the large 5th instar caterpillars are the easiest to spot. (A fifth instar caterpillar is a caterpillar that is full grown and will become a chrysalis with its next molt. See the section on monarch life cycle, pages 10 and 11, for more information.) They are big and showy, there is likely to be a pile of frass on the leaf below them that gives away their location if they are on the underside of the leaves, and they make huge holes in the leaves. However, if you are collecting for the classroom you should make an effort to collect younger specimens, even if you intend to use only fifth instar caterpillars with your students. Although it may take some practice to spot them, there are more earlier instar caterpillars and eggs in the wild than there are 5th instar caterpillars. Predation thins the population considerably. Making it all the way to 5th instar is quite a caterpillar accomplishment. Spiders, ants, assassin bugs and many other predators eat young caterpillars. Paper wasps are always on the prowl for caterpillars to cut up into pieces and stuff in their nests to feed their young. Wild caterpillars are often parasitized by tachinid flies. In some areas, a large percentage of the 5th instar caterpillars will be parasitized. It is frustrating to raise a caterpillar in your classroom only to have maggots crawl out of the chrysalis. Younger caterpillars have a better chance of not being parasitized yet. Parasitized caterpillars can add extra problems to your monarch rearing activities. The larval flies inside parasitized caterpillars will kill them as they hang in "j" or shortly after they make their chrysalis. Small maggots will descend from the dead caterpillar or pupa on silken threads and quickly form brown, pill-capsule shaped pupae of their own in the bottom of your caterpillar cage. The tachinid fly pupae will be camouflaged by frass in the bottom of the cage. If you don't get them cleaned out before they emerge as flies, they will mate and lay their eggs on other caterpillars in your monarch container.

The telltale thread left behind as tachinid maggots leave a dead chrysalis

adult tachinid fly, maggot and 2 pupae

If an area of milkweed was mowed earlier in the summer and has sprouted again, monarchs will tend to favor the tender, new growth over older, tough or moldy leaves. Many sources will tell you that monarchs lay their eggs on the under side of tender leaves near the top of milkweed plants. But they will also lay eggs on milkweed flowers and flower buds, on milkweed pods, on the top of leaves near the bottom of the plant or anywhere else on the plant that they please! My experience has been that individual monarch butterflies will tend to lay eggs in the same way. If you find an egg laid on a particular part of the plant, the butterfly that laid that egg has likely laid several others in similar positions on other plants in the area. Although they lay their eggs one at a time, monarchs, in mid to late summer when they are not actively migrating, may return to the same area day after day.

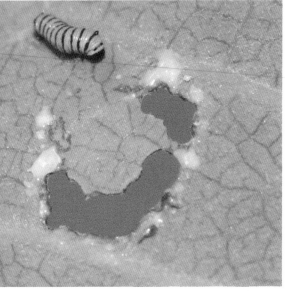

1st instar caterpillars chew holes in the middle of milkweed leaves

Milkweed bugs chew holes on the tips of leaves

Learn to read the chew signs on the milkweed. Chew holes indicate that something is eating the milkweed. In mid to late summer there are likely to be a number of chew marks on the milkweed. Larger monarch caterpillars make arched chew patterns from the edges of the leaf often completely consuming it (see page 30). Small chew holes in the middle of leaves are usually made by younger caterpillars. Chew holes on the very tips of milkweed leaves are usually the work of milkweed beetles. If you find whole leaves skeletonized most likely you are looking at the work of a cluster of milkweed tussock moth caterpillars.

Tussock moth caterpillar damage

Tips

- Avoid handling the monarch any more than necessary. Clip off the whole leaf with the caterpillar or egg on it and set it in your container. Or, if your container is large enough, clip off the stem of milkweed and wrap the end in moist paper towels and plastic.

- Don't carry large caterpillars and small caterpillars or eggs in the same container. The large caterpillars may accidentally eat the eggs and smaller caterpillars!

- Make sure that you don't leave the container exposed to sunlight. It could warm up fast. Caterpillars may quit eating and die when the temperatures get above 90° F.

Getting Monarchs from Labs and Breeders

In the last few years it has become easier and more cost effective to get monarch stock from labs and breeders. The advantage to this way of acquiring stock is that it is a bit more reliable, making it easier to schedule your classes. You must still keep a bit of flexibility in your schedule because these are still living creatures that will grow on their own schedule and availability can change and the provider cannot always control that. There are USDA regulations that restrict where monarch stock can be shipped. Contact any breeder or lab that you want to use well in advance. You should also be aware that shipping live critters can be expensive. Be sure to figure shipping costs into your budget.

Various diseases are serious issues for anyone who is raising and selling large quantities of monarchs. If you arrange to get stock from a new breeder in your area you might run into some of those problems. Labs and breeders that have been in business for a while generally have methods in place to monitor for disease and control it. For the most part, stock you receive from them is going to be healthy. When there are problems they are usually related to the shipping process: pressure changes, delays or exposure to en-route insecticide use. If your stock arrives dead, most suppliers will replace it, but it will be up to you to manage your monarchs properly when you get them. The vast majority of deaths occur because of mistakes that happen after you receive the stock. Breeders usually figure on about a 50% mortality from egg to adult. Though this may seem high, it is much better than the mortality rate in the wild. The mortality rate is tied to mass rearing techniques. Usually your shipment will contain a few extra eggs or caterpillars to make up for expected losses. Since you will typically be working with less than 100 individuals, with a little luck and patience you can significantly reduce the mortality in your stock. I recently raised a shipment of caterpillars and had a 130% survival rate! All of my extras made it too.

What to Do When the Caterpillars and Eggs Arrive

Always know where you are going to get fresh milkweed for your monarchs BEFORE you order any eggs or caterpillars.

Eggs from a breeder generally arrive tightly packed on tropical milkweed leaves. Tropical milkweed is easy to raise and use in breeding houses. The leaves are much smaller than the most common milkweeds in the north (common milkweed, *Asclepias syriaca* in the east and showy milkweed, *Asclepias speciosa,* in the mid-west and west). A tiny leaf two inches long and less than an inch wide can have thirty or more eggs on it! Monarchs in the breeding houses are still laying eggs one at a time, but many egg laying females are using the same limited number of plants. This is a practical advantage for the breeders, but can be quite a quandary for the teacher receiving the eggs.

If you have ordered eggs as a group and need to separate them, cut the milkweed leaf with an exacto blade to divide up the eggs as needed. Use a relatively small plastic container like the kind used for leftovers or take out salads in some restaurants. Any small container, large enough to lay a full sized milkweed leaf in will do. If the container is too large it will make it hard for you to track your caterpillars once they hatch and may dry out too easily. Wash two large common milkweed leaves and carefully check them for ants, mites or spiders. Pat them dry with an absorbent paper towel (like Bounty). Place the damp paper towel in the bottom of the container. Lay one milkweed leaf on top of the paper towel. Put the egg laden tropical milkweed leaf on top of the common milkweed leaf with the side with the majority of the eggs facing up. Place the other common milkweed leaf right side up on top. The newly hatched caterpillars seem to prefer the underside of the common milkweed leaves. Placing the second milkweed leaf right side up makes that side immediately available to the hatching caterpillars and they seem to wander off less. Close the container lid.

Check your eggs several times a day. If any mold or rotting occurs before the eggs hatch remove the affected material. Remove any standing water caused by condensation. When the eggs hatch the caterpillars will usually crawl up to the milkweed leaf above and start munching. They will spread out on their own and you will not have to handle them. Generally very few will travel down to the milkweed leaf underneath. You can wash the frass off of it and put it on top as fresh food after all of the eggs have hatched. As the eggs hatch, I separate out the caterpillars to create containers with no more than ten caterpillars in them.

Egg and Caterpillar Suppliers

Shady Oak Butterfly Farm

Shady Oak Butterfly Farm is a very reliable breeder. Run by Edith Smith, its extensive greenhouse and butterfly breeding houses are located in Florida. Edith's main business is butterfly releases but she is committed to education, She has recently created a teachers' section on her web site and is offering all stages of monarchs for classroom use.

http://www.buyabutterfly.com/

Monarch Watch

Monarch Watch out of the University of Kansas at http://www.monarchwatch.com/ is another very important site for teachers. Monarch Watch runs a tagging program and has been providing monarch caterpillars to teachers for quite a long time. They offer a Monarch Rearing Kit that contains between fourteen and sixteen first through third instar caterpillars.

Monarch Watch Shop

http://shop.monarchwatch.org/

The International Butterfly Breeder Association

The International Butterfly Breeder Association maintains a membership list of qualified breeders that could be used to locate a breeder in your area.

http://www.butterflybreeders.org

Classroom Logistics

Classroom Suggestions

There are as many ways to use monarchs in the classroom as there are teachers interested in using them!

Monarch study is a great way to introduce inquiry science for the year. Students can hone their observational skills and pose questions. The questions can be used to introduce the concept of testable questions. For example, an unanswerable question like, "Does my monarch like the color blue?" can be refined. The definition of "like" can be changed to a measurable quality. "Does a caterpillar grow better if it is exposed to the color blue?" Students can brainstorm how to test the growth of control caterpillars not exposed to the color blue with the growth of caterpillars exposed to the color blue. It is an opportunity to learn about variables as they make sure that all other factors in the two sets of caterpillars are identical. It is an opportunity to learn how to collect, analyze and present data. Graphing and math concepts can be introduced. Students can share observations and answer questions along with scientists and other students across the continent through Journey North, Monarch Watch, and Monarchs in the Classroom. (See page 36 for more information on Journey North, Monarch Watch and Monarchs in the Classroom.)

Monarchs can be an entry into studying ecosystems. The milkweed patch is a dynamic community that can be used to study food webs, energy flow and the interaction of organisms.

The changes that take place as the caterpillar metamorphoses are a great journaling focus.

Comparing the monarch life cycle to events in human experience can introduce the concept of metaphor.

Metamorphosis and change, as well as the butterfly and caterpillar patterns, present images that can be explored in art classes or used as an introduction to poetry.

The monarch migration can be used to introduce geography and social studies investigations as the students track the movement of monarch across the continent.

There are many programs available nationwide to support classroom use of monarchs. Web sites listed on page 36 include some of the more well established programs.

How Many Caterpillars?

There are many different ways to approach monarchs in your classroom. You can create a central display for all of the students, provide a caterpillar for each student to care for or provide several for a group of students. Each strategy has advantages and drawbacks.

A Caterpillar for Each Student

Students become very involved in their "own " caterpillars and pay closer attention to the changes it is going through. Individual caterpillars can be kept in clear plastic cups or plastic peanut butter jars with stocking or paper towel lids. This strategy is particularly helpful if you will be asking your students to keep daily data on their monarch as it is much easier to keep track of individual caterpillars. It is also a good way to control disease in the classroom monarch population because one sick caterpillar will not infect the others. However since mortality is a very real possibility, dealing with a dead caterpillar can present a problem especially for very young students.

Several Caterpillars for a Group

Having small groups of students care for several caterpillars can reduce the personal loss in the case of mortality. Three to four caterpillars can be kept in a small insect box or other container. Removing direct ownership can reduce the impact of a loss. It also provides a small group of insects for students to track for inquiry purposes.

A Classroom Display

A dozen or so caterpillars shared by the entire class in an aquarium or large bug box is a good way to introduce students to monarch caterpillars and butterflies. Choose a place where students can easily observe what is going on in the container.

Containers

A monarch caterpillar can be raised in any container in which it can be given enough milkweed to eat and in which it can fully expand its wings once it emerges from its chrysalis. You will need to clean the frass out of the container daily and make sure there is enough fresh milkweed. For individual student caterpillars, clear plastic cups and peanut butter jars work. Other containers include aquariums, bug boxes, rubbermaid tubs, and clear 2-liter soda bottles with the bottoms cut off and slid back on upside down. Old panty hose with runs make great lids with good ventilation and a reasonably good surface for pupation. Plastic lids for cups or jars can be cut and fitted with screening material. Use your imagination, you may have a perfect container that no one else has thought of before!

CARE AND PRECAUTIONS

- Avoid over crowding. To cut down on the likelihood of disease wiping out an entire collection of monarchs, keep even fairly large container groups down to a dozen caterpillars.

- Clean out frass and any rotting milkweed every day.

- Avoid handling very small caterpillars. Cut off the part of the leaf they are on if it is starting to go bad, or lay a well chewed up leaf that has caterpillars on it onto a whole leaf.

- Be sure to provide fresh milkweed for your caterpillar at all times.

- Do not handle caterpillars, pupae or butterfly if you spend a good bit of time in contact with a pet that has been treated with Advantage or any other tick and flea preparation that might get on your hands.

- Do not move a caterpillar that is about to shed. Look at the head capsule to see if it is about to shed.

- Be cautious about moving a caterpillar that is hanging in "J." If the filaments have gone limp, it will be shedding its skin soon— don't transport that caterpillar's container. Jostling it as it is trying to attach the cremaster to its silk button can be disastrous.

- Leave chrysalides hanging where the butterfly can emerge and hang to expand its wings. If the chrysalis has fallen and cannot be tied up or attached by it cremaster with hot glue to a flexible surface, at very least leave it on a surface that it can crawl a very short distance and hang from...such as a paper towel draped over the edge of a container with plenty of clearance for the butterfly to expand its wings. The butterfly will not immediately begin to fly. You will have a couple of hours to get it into an enclosure after it has emerged.

WEB SITES

There are quite a few excellent monarch and insect related sites. This is only a starting point.

Monarch Watch   http://www.monarchwatch.org

Monarch Watch is the longest standing monarch support program for classrooms. It is run by Orley "Chip" Taylor out of the University of Kansas. Monarch Watch maintains D-Plex, a listserv for monarch enthusiasts. It conducts an annual monarch tagging program that is open to the public. If you want to participate in tagging it is advisable to order tags as early as possible. They become available in August and are usually bought up quickly. The Monarch Watch web site contains a great deal of information on monarchs, research and milkweed in an accessible format. Monarch Watch maintains an online store with many classroom aids, including live stock.

Monarchs in the Classroom and Monarch Lab   http://www.monarchlab.org
and Monarch Larva Monitoring Project   http://www.mlmp.org/

Run by Karen Oberhauser at the University of Minnesota. These are both excellent teacher support sites and programs.

Monarchs in the Classroom puts out a very informative annual newsletter that is available in PDF form on line at Monarch Lab. It is an excellent resource for current research and maintains an online store selling excellent curriculum guides and a number of classroom support materials. MITC offers excellent teacher training courses for Minnesota teachers that are underwritten by the State of Minnesota. A limited number of out of state teachers are accepted into these programs.

The Monarch Larva Monitoring Program is a continent wide citizen science program that collects information on the population dynamics in milkweed patches. The annual newsletter is excellent and available in PDF form on line.

Journey North/Journey South http://www.learner.org/jnorth/monarch/index.html

This program, run by Elizabeth Howard, is one of the most teacher and student friendly inquiry-based science sites available. The monarch portion of this program is excellent and there are several other programs as well. Journey North runs the Symbolic Monarch Migration, an exciting exchange program with students in Mexico City and the monarch reserve area. The deadline for program entries is always in early October so be sure to check it out early. It also provides weekly updates on the monarch migration both north and south with inquiry questions for classroom participants, intensive interviews and write ups on various cultural and real life events in the monarch reserves, as well as opportunities for students to participate by adding their observations to those of other students across the continent. These are all free and require only a registration. Annual program evaluations are requested.

Project Monarch Health http://www.monarchparasites.org

Project Monarch Health is a citizen science survey of the occurrence of the protozoan parasite *Ophryocistis elektroscirrha* (*Oe*), which parasitizes monarchs. The web site includes a lot of great information that will be useful for anyone keeping monarchs in captivity.

Bas Relief, LLC http://www.basrelief.org

This is my site providing wholesale and retail access to this text, *Milkweed Monarchs and More: A Field Guide to the Invertebrate Community in the Milkweed Patch, Monarch Come Play with Me,* and *Milkweed Visitors*, as well as free teacher and parent guides to using the books.

Shady Oak Butterfly Farm's teacher's site http://www.teachingwithmonarchs.com/buying.html

Run by Edith Smith, this site offers live monarchs, painted ladies and other species in all stages and information on using them in the classroom.

A MONARCH CLASSROOM BIBLIOGRAPHY

The following books may be useful for those planning to use monarchs in the classroom.

MONARCH AND BUTTERFLY LITERATURE WRITTEN PRIMARILY FOR CHILDREN

Arnosky, Jim. *Crinkleroot's Guide to Knowing Butterflies and Moths.* New York: Simon and Schuster, 1996.
Whimsical combination how to book and field guide on butterflies and moths.

Boring, Mel. Linda Garrow (Illustrator). *Caterpillars, Bugs and Butterflies*. Minnetonka, Minnesota: NorthWord Press, 1996.
Children's insect field guide.

Bunting, Eve. Greg Shed (Illustrator). *Butterfly House.* New York: Scholastic, 1999.
This is the story of a young girl who, with her grandpa, makes a special house for a painted lady caterpillar. Great illustrations, nice concept.

Carle, Eric. *The Very Hungry Caterpillar.* New York: Philomel, 1987.
Excellent picture book for early introduction to caterpillars.

Coville, Bruce. John Clapp(Illustrator). *The Prince of Butterflies.* New York: Harcourt Inc., 2002.
Beautifully illustrated, rich fantasy about a boy who help monarchs find an alternative resting place when their normal one is destroyed by construction.

George, Jean Craighead. Kam Mak (Illustrator). *Moon of the Monarch Butterflies.* New York: Harper Collins Publishers, 1993.
Beautiful story about interconnected nature along the path of a monarch's spring migration.

Glaser, Linda. Gay Holland (Illustrator). *Magnificent Monarchs.* Brookfield, Connecticut: Millbrook Press, 2000.
Story of the monarch life cycle and migration. Beautiful soft illustrations.

Himmelman, John. *A Monarch Butterfly's Life.* New York: Children's Press, 1999.
Nice bold illustrations of life cycle and migration.

Holland, Mary. *Milkweed Visitors.* Glenshaw, Pennsylvania: Bas Relief Publishing Group, 2006
A beautifully photographed introduction to the milkweed community.

Johnston, Tony. Susan Guevara (Illustrator). ***Isabel's House of Butterflies.*** San Francisco: Sierra Club Books for Children, 2003.
Beautiful illustrated story about a Mexican peasant girl who saves an oyamel fir tree next to her house that monarchs come to each year. This story line is a little loose on reality but a nice starting place for discussion.

Lasky, Kathryn. Christopher G. Knight (Illustrator). ***Monarchs.*** New York: A Gulliver Green Book, Harcourt Brace and Company, 1993.
Several rich story lines about monarchs and people who interact with them.

Lavies, Bianca. Monarch Butterflies, ***Mysterious Travelers.*** New York: Dutton, 1992.
Story of the discovery of the monarch reserves by the photographer from National Geographic who was there.

Llewellyn, Claire. Simon Mendez (illustrator). ***Starting Life: Butterfly***. Minnetonka, MN: North Word, 2003.
Excellent, well-organized and well-illustrated introduction the life history of the monarch butterfly.

Madison, Alan. Kevin Hawkes (Illustrator). ***velma gratch and the way cool butterfly.*** New York, NY: Schwarz and Wade Books, 2007.
This delightful tale of a 1st grader trying to be as memorable as her sisters serves as a simple introduction to the study of butterflies and the monarch butterfly in particular with only a touch of over the top exaggeration.

O'Flatharta, Antoine. Meilo So. (Illustrator) ***Hurry and the Monarch***. New York: Alfred A. Knopf, 2005.
Story of the monarch migration integrated with the over wintering strategy of Hurry, a Texas tortoise.

Polacco, Patricia. ***The Butterfly.*** New York: Philomel Books, 2000.
The monarch butterfly is woven into this story of two girls in Nazi Germany.

Pringle, Laurence. Bob Marstall (Illustrator). ***An Extraordinary Life: The Story of a Monarch Butterfly.*** New York: Orchard Books, 1997.
Beautifully illustrated, follows the life of a monarch butterfly from egg through migration and return.

Rea, Ba. ***Monarch Come Play with Me.*** Glenshaw, Pennsylvania: Bas Relief Publishing Group, 2006.
An introduction to the life cycle of a monarch butterfly for a pre-K through second grade audience with an emphasis on the similarities and differences between a child's and the monarch's growth and activities.

Ryder, Joanne. Lynne Cherry (Illustrator). ***Where Butterflies Grow.*** New York: Puffin Books, 1999.
Beautiful, poetic telling of the black swallowtails life history.

ACTIVITY AND WORKBOOKS

Mikula, Rick. ***The Family Butterfly Book.*** North Adams, Massachusetts: Storey Publishing, 2000.
Projects, activities and a field guide.

Muther, Connie. ***My Monarch Journal.*** Nevada City, California: Dawn Publications. 2000.
Journal illustrated with excellent photographs.

Rea, Ba. Leah Spink. ***My Monarch Investigation.*** Harmony, Pennsylvania: Lifestrands, 2002.
Journal designed to go with curriculum using monarchs as a vehicle for teaching inquiry science methods.

Rosenblatt, Lynn. ***Monarch Magic!: Butterfly Activities and Nature Discoveries*** Williamson Publishing, 1998.
Monarch related activities and life cycle information to use with children.

MONARCH LITERATURE WRITTEN PRIMARILY FOR ADULTS

Halpern, Susan. Four ***Wings and a Prayer.*** New York: Pantheon Books, 2001.
Excellent very humanizing overview of the people and the science of monarch research.

Manos-Jones, Maraleen. ***The Spirit of Butterflies: Myth, Magic and Art***. New York: Harry Abrams, Inc., 2000.
Beautifully illustrated look at butterflies in art through history.

Marent, Thomas. ***butterfly.*** New York, NY: DK Publishing, 2008.
An extravagantly beautiful photographic introduction to the lives of butterflies.

Mikula, Rick. ***Garden Butterflies of North America.*** Minocqua, WI:Willow Creek Press, 1997.
Introduction to butterfly gardens and the butterflies that inhabit them.

Oberhauser, Karen and Michelle Solensky, Editors. ***The Monarch Butterfly, Biology and Conservation.*** Ithaca, New York: Cornell University Press, 2004.
Compilation of scientific papers on monarch science.

Pyle, Robert Michael. ***Chasing Monarchs: Migrating with the Butterflies of Passage.*** New York: Houghton Mifflin, 1999.
Detailed account of a travels to observe the monarch migration in the west.

Urquhart, Fred. ***The Monarch Butterfly: International Traveler.*** Ellison Bay, Wisconsin: Wm Caxton LTD, 1998.
The work of Dr. Fred Urquhart. A classic in monarch research, includes some early misconceptions along with discoveries.

CURRICULA AND MATERIAL ON EDUCATION

Oberhauser, Karen, Monarchs in the Classroom. ***Monarchs and More, An Inquiry and Anthropod Based Curriculum.*** St. Paul, Minnesota: University of Minnesota, 2008.
Separate guides for Grades K-2, Grades 3-6, and Middle School each include age-specific lessons divided into 6 sections on butterfly life cycles, butterfly systematics, ecology, conservation, conducting experiments, and monarch migration. Each Guide includes extensive background information, with sections on monarch biology, practical tips for rearing and observing insects, and conducting inquiry-based lessons in the classroom.

Pearce, Charles. ***Nurturing Inquiry.*** Portsmouth, NH: Heinemann, 1999.
Treatise on using inquiry science methods in schools.

Sobel, David. ***Beyond Ecophobia: Reclaiming the Heart in Nature Education.*** Great Barrington, Massachusetts: Orion Society, 1996.
Discussion of environmental education.

FIELD GUIDES

Forey, Pamela. Cecilia Fitzsimons. *An Instant Guide to Butterflies.* New York: Bonanza Books, 1987. Field guide.

McGavin, George C.. *Insects, Spiders and other Terrestrial Arthropods.* New York: Dorling Kindersley, 2000.
Field guide.

Mikula, Rick. *The Family Butterfly Book.* North Adams, Massachusetts: Storey Publishing, 2000.
Projects, activities and a field guide.

Oberhauser, Karen. Kristen Kuda (Illustrator). *A Field Guide to Monarch Caterpillars.* University of Minnesota 1997.
Field guide to the 5 instars of monarch caterpillars.

Pyle, Robert Michael. *National Audubon Society Field Guide to Butterflies.* New York: Alfred A, Knopf, 1981.
Field guide.

Rea, Ba. Karen Oberhauser, Mike Quinn. *Milkweed Monarchs and More: A Field Guide to the Invertebrate Community in the Milkweed Patch.* Glenshaw: Pennsylvania: Bas Relief Publishing Group, 2003.
Field guide of the monarch and milkweed community, small field use version.

Rea, Ba. Karen Oberhauser, Mike Quinn. *The Updated and Enlarged Second Edition of Milkweed Monarchs and More: A Field Guide to the Invertebrate Community in the Milkweed Patch.* Union, West Virginia: Bas Relief, LLC, 2010.
An updated edition of the original field guide of the monarch and milkweed community enlarged to 8 X 10 inches to facilitate use in classrooms.

Schenck, Marcus. *Butterflies*. Emmaus, Pennsylvania: Rodale Press, 1990.
Field Guide.

Stokes, Donald and Lillian. *Stokes Butterfly Book.* Boston: Little, Brown, 1991.
Butterfly gardening and field guide.

Wagner, David L. et al. *Caterpillars of Eastern Forests.* Morgantown, West Virginia: United States Department of Agriculture, 1997.
Field guide.

Wright, Amy Bartlett. *Peterson's First Guide to Caterpillars.* Boston: Houghton Mifflin, 1993.
Field guide.

GLOSSARY

abdomen - name for the hind body part of an insect

adult - final stage of insect metamorphosis

antenna - a sense organ than can pick up vibrations and sense chemicals

biomass - the weight of living things in a community

caterpillar - larval stage of moths and butterflies

chrysalis (plural: chrysalides or alternatively: chrysalid)- pupa stage of moths and butterflies

community - the organisms that live in a given area

competing consumers - organisms that depend on the same food source.

compound eye - complex multi faceted eye of insects

cremaster - black stick like feature with which a monarch chrysalis attaches to a silk button to hang while it pupates

crochets - small hooks on the foot of a caterpillar's prolegs

cuticle - another word for exoskeleton

diptera - flies; means two wings; of flies: dipteran

eclose - to emerge from an egg or pupal stage

egg - the first stage in insect metamorphosis

exoskeleton - tough outer layer of an insect, sometimes called the cuticle

filaments - black, fleshy tentacles at the front and back of a monarch caterpillar

food web - a model for how energy passes through a natural community

frass - caterpillar droppings

habitat - the place where an organism can find everything it needs to survive

haltere - modified pair of vestigial wings on flies

head - first of three parts of an insect body

head capsule - exoskeleton covering of head on a caterpillar

hemolymph - insect blood

herbivore - organism that eat plants

insectivore - predator that eats insects

instar - stage of larval development of insects determined by the number of times it has molted its exoskeleton: newly hatched is 1st instar; molted once is 2nd instar etc.

maggot - larval stage of a fly

mandible - insect mouth part

metamorphosis - stages of insect development

    complete metamorphosis - 4 stage metamorphosis: egg, larva, pupa, adult

    incomplete metamorphosis - 3 stage metamorphosis: egg, nymph, adult; sometimes called simple metamorphosis

nectivore - insect that drinks nectar

nymph - 2nd stage in incomplete metamorphosis

ocelli - simple insect eyes that detect light and dark

parasite - organism that lives on or in another organism which it consumes

photosynthesis - a process carried out by chlorophyll in green plants through which the energy from sunlight is captured in the chemical bonds in sugars

predator - an animal that eats other animals

proboscis - long straw-like mouth of a butterfly

producer - name for green plants which make food from sunlight

prolegs - 5 pairs of fleshy back legs on caterpillars

pupa - the third, largely immobile, stage in complete metamorphosis

reproductive diapause - the state of sexual immaturity of the migrating generation of monarch butterflies

scavenger - organism that eats detritus, dead plants and animals and waste material

spinneret - an invertebrate organ that produces silk thread; found on spiders, caterpillars and other larval insects

spiracle - the outer opening of an insect's respiratory system

tarsi - insect feet (singular: tarsus)

thorax - the central of three body parts of an insect to which legs and wings attach.

true legs - the six insect legs of caterpillars as distinct from prolegs

Made in the USA
Charleston, SC
11 July 2011